Contents

Page

Introduction to your *Handy Guide to Facilitation*

1

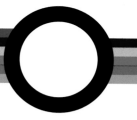

Introduction

If you are involved in improvement work, you may at some point be asked to facilitate a group meeting or workshop to discuss how to improve services for patients.

If you are new to this sort of work, you may well have all sorts of questions about how to make these group sessions as productive as possible.

This guide is designed to give you the know-how and confidence to effectively facilitate workshops and group meetings. You will find lots of things to consider and practical tips, including:

- advice to help you prepare for your role as a facilitator
- tools and techniques to choose from according to how you want to run your workshop or meeting

Handy hint for USING THIS GUIDE

As you work your way through this guide, think about your role, the work of the group you are facilitating and your relationship with the people in that group. Ask yourself:

- Are you clear about the anticipated outcomes and specific questions on which the group will focus?

- Who are you linking with for this improvement work?

- Is the work of the group part of an organisational or national initiative?

- Are you normally part of the group and know the individuals and their work really well or are you to be an 'external' facilitator?

- Are you the group leader? If not what is your relationship with the person who leads the group you are going to work with?

- Do you need to engage others beforehand who will help strengthen your relationship with the group?

A Handy Guide to Facilitation

02

What is facilitation and how can it help with improvement work?

2

2 What is facilitation and how can it help with improvement work?

Facilitation is the art and science of helping groups in their thinking, planning and decision-making. Bringing this level of clarity to group discussions about service improvement can have a significant impact on the quality of services provided to patients.

Understanding the impact of effective group work

We are all involved in group meetings and have been since we were very young.

- Think about the groups you were involved in as a child - the brownies, the scouts, your 'gang' of friends or the youth club. What made you want to go back and continue being part of the group or did you leave after just a few meetings?

- Now think of different group meetings at work. Did you feel bored or excited about what was being discussed? Did you feel involved or left out?

- Think of the people who led these groups. Did you like them? Did they make you feel important? Did you feel they were 'in control'?

Task

Think of two groups you have been involved in, one that you enjoyed and one you did not. Make notes about your experiences. It doesn't matter if it was a work group or a social group.

A group you enjoyed	A group you didn't enjoy
What made you enjoy it?	**What made you not enjoy it?**

Research into the characteristics of effective groups has identified a number of qualities. Check these against your own experiences.

In an effective group:

- The task, objective or the reason for people to meet is well understood by everyone.
- The atmosphere of the group tends to be informal, comfortable and relaxed.
- There is much discussion in which everyone participates.
- Everyone listens to each other.
- People are free to express their feelings as well as their ideas.
- Disagreement and criticism is frequent and frank but the group is comfortable with this and shows no signs of avoiding the conflict.
- Decisions are reached by a consensus in which it is clear that everyone is in general agreement.
- When action is taken, clear assignments are made and accepted.
- The leader of the group does not dominate but is in control.

In contrast, group work that doesn't work well will:

- Be dominated by a few individuals and their perspectives.
- Never hear the ideas and comments from the quiet members.
- Take too long to get to the real agenda.
- Have no clear objectives.
- Have no follow-up actions.

Be clear about:

- Goals – are they the same for everyone?
- Roles – what do you want people to do?
- Procedure – how are things going to happen?

Ask yourself:

- Are everyone's expectations the same?

Remember that:

- As a facilitator, you are not chairing a meeting or debate.
- Facilitation is not about offering counselling or group therapy.
- Your role as a facilitator is not as teacher or trainer.

Getting the balance right

To ensure your role as facilitator is as successful as it can be, you should consider the type of group meeting you are planning and what you want to achieve from it. Think about:

- *Formality* – do you need a formal group to accomplish a specific task or an informal group that is more spontaneous and evolving?

- *Climate* – how close and friendly or casual should the group interaction be?

- *Participation* – what should the interaction be like? How much and what type of engagement do you want?

- *Conflict* – How will you deal with conflict and disagreements?

- *Decision-making* – how will decisions be made and by whom?

- *Responsibilities* – how will tasks be assigned and sub-groups formed?

- *Communication* – what channels are preferred and how is the group networked? Do they prefer face-to-face meetings, phone calls or email?

- *Evaluation* – how will progress be monitored, checked and evaluated? How will feedback be provided?

To be an effective facilitator, you need to match:

- individual preference and group experience
- the purpose or task with the process of engagement and
- your own skills and experience with the design of the meeting.

Understanding the group you are working with

Whatever the group and for whatever length of time it is planning to work together, you need to be aware that groups usually go through a series of stages before becoming truly effective.

This is not a simple linear process and new people joining may cause the group to go back to the beginning.

Stages of group development
Forming   Storming   Norming   Performing Adjourning

Adapted from Tuckman and Jenson (1977)

The stages of group development explained

Forming
Effort at this stage is spent on defining goals. At this stage individuals may be confused as to why they are in the group and be trying to size up the personal benefits relative to the personal costs of being involved. They may be keeping their feelings to themselves.

Storming
This is the stage when team members test each other. They question values, behaviours, tasks and relative priorities of the goals, as well as who is to be responsible for what. There may also be questioning of the guidance and direction of the leader and some members may withdraw and isolate themselves either from the emotional tension or because they recognise that their values, beliefs and skills don't fit. If the storming is not allowed to happen, the team may never perform well. It is a healthy process in which a team evolves with a common set of values, beliefs and goals.

Norming
This is when behaviour progressively develops into an acceptance of differences of opinion and the ground rules and decision-making processes are accepted. This is the time when individuals in the group 'value the difference' that others bring.

Performing

During this stage, the group effectively and efficiently works together and towards the goals. The group and individuals learn and develop together. You could describe this stage as 'less me, more we!'

Adjourning

This is the end of the working life of the group. Some groups such as improvement project teams are created to work with specific problems for a set time e.g. six months or a year. They should have a well-defined and managed ending where group members know what to expect and are helped to deal with it and move on. Sometimes members feel sad, nostalgic and 'mourn' the end of the group.

Pause
and reflect

Take a moment to consider what you have read in the guide so far. Ask yourself which of the following outcomes could be considered a good group experience:

Outcome	Good group experience? (circle as appropriate)
The objectives have been met	Yes / No
The objectives have been met but every individual felt railroaded and threatened	Yes / No
The objectives have not been met	Yes / No
The objectives have not been met but individuals had a better understanding of themselves, each other and the problem	Yes / No

03

Preparing for your role as a facilitator

3 Preparing for your role as a facilitator

There is a growing awareness that groups, when well managed, can unleash an incredible enthusiasm for doing things better and differently. Facilitation plays an important role in helping groups to work effectively and also, therefore, in bringing about improvements in healthcare.

Facilitation requires:

- an environment of mutual trust
- the ability to generate a sharing environment
- a willingness to listen
- a desire to seek understanding
- the ability to be diverse and flexible
- the ability to challenge yet stay supportive
- the ability to work with people from a wide range of backgrounds and
- a toolkit of styles, approaches and techniques.

To be effective as a facilitator, you should help the group you are working with get further, faster and in a more focused way than they would alone – and help them have some fun along the way!

Pause
and reflect

Before starting to prepare for your role as a facilitator, take a moment to reflect on the purpose of the workshop or group meeting. You are most likely to want your meetings to provoke conversations, agree actions or both.

Think carefully about this before going any further as different facilitation tools and techniques are needed for different situations. For example, the skills and tools you need for facilitated exploration and learning will be different to those needed for facilitated action and agreement.

How to design a facilitated group meeting

Taking the time in the early stages to carefully plan and design your workshop will ensure there are no surprises on the day and that your meeting runs as smoothly as possible. You should think carefully about:

- What is expected and how realistic it is given the group and the time you have.

- The aims, anticipated outcomes and specific questions on which you will focus.

- Meeting and enlisting the help of the key people and a sample of the participants to find out about their history, problems and expectations.

- Choosing the right style of event and planning the agenda.

- How to get people to come to the meeting.

- Dates, location, room, layout, seating, refreshments, etc.

- How you can use those with experience, skills and knowledge.

- Preparation or pre-reading for participants.

- The right group activities (some activities you may find helpful are given later in this guide).

- Draft ground rules - there are different ways to do this. You could get the group to develop its own but this takes time. Another way is to suggest pre-prepared ground rules as a starting point and ask the group for any additional points or things they do not agree with.

- The budget.

- Evaluating and learning from the process impact and outcomes of the meeting.

Handy hint for EFFECTIVE FACILITATION

Some examples of ground rules you may wish to establish for your workshops include:

- Listen to others and value the diversity of opinions in the group.

- Be constructive.

- Value the differences: there is no right or wrong, no good or bad.

- Be open and honest.

- Recognise that this is the start of an improvement journey, not a destination.

- Keep to agreed times, especially the start and finish.

Ground rules should clearly state what is required, what is prohibited and what is permitted.

Enlisting the help of others

As you start to prepare for your facilitated meeting, you may wish to enlist the help of others and set up a 'design team'. A design team is a group of between five and 15 people representing participants of all levels and professions. Together you should consider:

Purpose	• What are the objectives and how do they relate to the overall goals of the department, organisation or improvement initiative? • How will the meeting transform the inputs into the desired outcomes? • What will be different because this meeting took place?
Inputs	• Who are the invited participants? • Who will be the facilitator, speakers, chair, etc. and who will brief them? • What are the concerns, issues, desires and motives of both the participants and the organisers?
Activities (process)	• What set of activities will produce the purpose and achieve the outcome? Consider discussions, information sharing, group work. • How do we accommodate different learning styles?
Outcomes	• What are the desired ideas, mood and attitudes of the participants when they leave? • How will you evaluate?

When you have considered each of these elements of your workshop, you should then take each activity that is planned for the day in turn and think carefully about each of the following aspects:

Time	Start and end of each activity.
Issue/Topic	What participants can expect.
Lead	Who is to lead each activity and what is their role? Who will be in supporting roles?
Format	Plenary, table work, group, discussion, etc.
What is needed	Flip charts, pens, Post-it notes, etc.
Objective	What is the objective and how does it contribute to the goal of the whole meeting?

Remember that you need to decide who from the design team will do what to prepare for the meeting and each activity planned for it.

Case study
Using a 'design team' to plan and deliver events

Members of the Critical Care National Programme Team looked for a new way of involving key stakeholders in the planning and execution of their national sharing event. The resulting 'design team' consisted of volunteers from the programme's service improvement network teams across England. Members attended monthly meetings and contributed their ideas, support and enthusiasm. The plan for the event was updated after each meeting and used as the main tool for problem-solving and communication. The banner headline 'Sharing without walls' was suggested by a member of the team and was one of many good ideas that contributed to the success of the event.

Advantages of design teams

- Teams are inclusive and democratic
- Talent can be identified and nurtured
- Members are exposed to new experiences and processes
- Teams provide an excellent quality assurance mechanism
- Planning is kept tight and on time
- New ideas are revealed
- Unlikely sources of help are identified
- Members can gain confidence to run their own events
- Teams provide an excellent arena for testing different project management methods
- Communication is improved
- 'Buy-in' is increased
- Teams ensure that the event agenda is relevant

Disadvantages of design teams

- Reasonably heavy time commitment
- Travel constraints can be frustrating
- There is some repetition if membership constantly changes
- Confusion and conflict can result if badly facilitated or chaired

Task

Do a 'dry run' of your planned workshop ahead of the day itself. By doing this, you will get to try out any tools and techniques that may be new or unfamiliar to you. Ask your friends and family or a group of people you know very well to be the participants for your dry run.

The amount of time you invest in your dry run will depend on your experience and confidence as a facilitator and the tools and techniques you have chosen to use.

Putting your preparation into practice

By the very nature of your role as a facilitator, you are part of the group you are facilitating but at the same time, you should remain separate from it. To manage this complex situation, it is essential that you establish clear boundaries for yourself and the group you are working with.

As you put all the hard work of planning and designing your workshop into practice, you should remember:

- Facilitation is hard work! If possible, have a supporting colleague with you at the workshop.

- Listen, acknowledge ideas and capture all suggestions and comments made from each person in the group.

- Observe all non-verbal communication.

- Notice the energy levels and take a short break or change the activity if energy levels are low.

- Start and finish on time including breaks - if you really need to run over, only do it with the consent of the group.

- Reconfirm the finish time at the start.

To effectively handle discussions that arise during the course of your workshop:

- Never colour your facilitation with your own views - this is the best way to lose the group's confidence.

- Clarify each point because if you don't understand a comment made, others in the group may not either.

- Help the group spot connections and overall themes.

- Summarise using the words of the participants, check it back and record it even if it seems odd to you. Avoid biased or selective summarising.

- Probe general statements such as "we need improved communication" or "I want better quality of care" by asking for examples to explain.

- Use language familiar to the group - you don't want to set yourself apart and lose their confidence in you.

- Avoid 'death by feedback' by keeping feedback from group activities short, set a time limit and keep to it.

- Think about the pace and direction of your workshop and the mood of participants.

- Move the group on when stuck on one issue.

- Remind the group often of the question being discussed.

- Keep an eye on the time and be ready for midway programme redesign if needed.

When drawing the workshop to a close, ensure you leave enough time to:

- Replay to the group what they have been doing - the initial objectives, starting point, questions, themes of discussion and the activities.

- Agree and record the actions and 'what's next' including how the notes of the session are going to be circulated.

- Gain immediate feedback by asking the group:
  - Did the workshop meet your expectations?
  - Did it meet the objectives of the session?
  - What would you have liked to be different?
  - What would you have liked more of?
  - What would you have liked less of?
  - What have you learnt?
  - Is there anything that you are still concerned or confused about?

Reviewing your facilitated workshop

As a facilitator, your role extends beyond the end of the group meeting. After each workshop you facilitate, you should debrief, review and evaluate the content in order to feedback to participants the impact your meeting has had on the improvement aim. You should also take the time to reflect on your experience and role as a facilitator to learn for the future.

There are two evaluation approaches to consider, which are:

- *Formative* - this approach gauges the contribution of activities during the programme. The focus here is on the process.

- *Summative* – this approach gauges the contribution of the activities at the end of the programme. The focus here is on outcomes.

Give good consideration to your evaluation in advance of your workshop and plan the approach you are going to take.

Pause and reflect

As part of the evaluation process, you should take the time to stop and ask yourself:

- What was going on?
- What did you see and hear?
- How did you feel?
- What sense can you make of your thoughts and feelings?
- How can you build on this for next time?

04

Facilitating a workshop or group meeting

4 Facilitating a workshop or group meeting

There are various styles you can adopt when facilitating a workshop, ranging from doing nothing to directing a group. It is important that you strike a balance between these different styles as too much direction can lead to a loss of group 'ownership' of the process and outcomes but too little direction can lead to confusion and frustration.

The overall objective of your workshop, the profile of the group you will be working with and your own personal preferences will all help you to choose the right facilitation style.

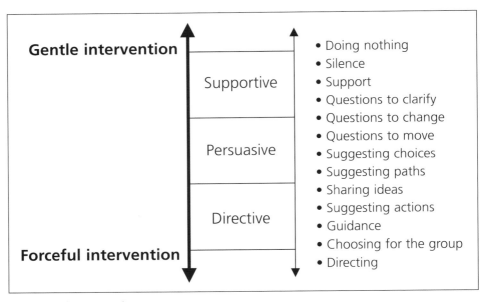

Adapted from Bentley 2001

Understanding the group you will be facilitating
Critical to your success as a facilitator is the knowledge you have of the group ahead of your workshop. When doing your homework on the group, you should consider:

- How large the group will be

- What their relationship to each other is

- Who the opinion leaders and key stakeholders are and if they will be there

- Whether the workshop is part of a series or a one-off event

- How interested people not present on the day will be identified and engaged

- What type of facilitation is expected and whether this matches what is required

- How the group will decide whether they have achieved what they wanted to

When researching your group, think about the individual participants and not just the group. Ask yourself:

- What might people want and what may they not want?
- How will they feel being with the others in the group?
- Do they actually want to be there as part of the group?
- What does each participant bring in terms of skills, knowledge and experience?
- What is each participant expecting to take away from the meeting?

The key to being an effective facilitator is being able to adapt and flex your style so that you can make an emotional and psychological connection with the members of your group. Take a moment to reflect on your own style and personal preferences and to understand the impact these have on those you are working with.

By taking the time to do this, you will become more effective at working with others and a more confident and competent facilitator.

Your key responsibilities as a facilitator

To be an effective facilitator, you must be prepared to:

• Support
• Challenge
• Interrupt
• Clarify
• Summarise
• Take risks and
• Guard the time

Your interaction with the group

During the course of a workshop, you will move through different stages of contact with the group you are working with. You may well change or adapt your style at the different stages, which are outlined below.

The different stages of contact with a group

Pre-contact
This begins with the request for facilitation. At this stage, depending on your experience you will probably need to be quite persuasive or even directive in making initial recommendations about the process and organisation of the workshop.

Contact
This is the first face-to-face engagement you will have with the group you are facilitating. The effect of this contact will vary with different individuals in the group. You can probably remember a time when your first impressions of a facilitator were either very good or not very good from the first few minutes.

Participants will form opinions quickly, so think carefully about:
• How you wish to appear
• How you introduce yourself
• How to establish your credibility
• How you present and gain agreement for the suggested ground rules
• How you state the aim of the session and its place in the bigger picture
• Your first activity and if you should use an ice breaker
• How you establish expectations
• How you get participants to introduce themselves

This is a particularly important stage in the facilitation process as you never get a second chance to make a first impression!

Full contact

This is the stage when there is meaningful discussion and debate. There may also be disagreement and conflict. Your style and what is required from you as the facilitator at this stage will definitely depend on how the group is working together. Be prepared to change your style and plans at short notice!

Post contact

This happens after the meeting when you need to debrief, review and evaluate. You will either do this with the design team or the group leaders. Don't forget your self-reflection as part of the debrief. Remember to agree exactly what is required and expected from you and others as post workshop support.

Case study

A facilitator was supporting a programme and the programme leader at their first key improvement workshop. An agenda had been agreed with the three key speakers who were to briefly introduce the day and outline the problem from their perspective. These initial talks went on for twice as long as they were supposed to and they did not respond to hints to end their presentations.

The facilitator felt the participants were getting restless, bored and frustrated at being brought together to be 'talked at'. When the session was handed over to him, he became directive - not his usual facilitating style. He abandoned the agenda and his introductory presentation and asked the participants to break for coffee. On their return he had the participants start working in small groups to discuss the issues raised.

The evaluation reflected that the decision was correct. The length of the talks was not appreciated but participants found that the group work led to the outcome of the day being achieved.

Improvement workshop, London

Handy hint for
EFFECTIVE FACILITATION

Be clear about what can and cannot be achieved as part of the workshop and set and manage expectations by contracting with the group. Ask them:

- What must you get from today?
- What do you need from other participants?
- What do you promise yourself?
- What do you need from me as your facilitator?

Ensure the autonomy of the group

To be successful as a facilitator, you need to ensure the group does not become too dependent on you. Your aim should be to ensure the group is self-sufficient, maintains its existing leadership and manages its own agenda.

The nature of group work means that people often come together out of interest or expertise in a given area. These groups, formed across departmental or organisational boundaries, bring together people of different professions and roles to improve the patient journey and learn together. These groups will be full of leaders and the skill of the facilitator is to help them work effectively together.

Think about ways to:

- Involve leaders in the design team.

- Show how different parts of the system fit together, interrelate and have equal importance.

- Raise awareness and debate about leadership within the group. Help everyone to understand that in groups, especially large groups, leadership is usually a shared responsibility.

- Use the questionnaire in the 'activities' section of this guide to help people think about their own communication style and the preferred style of others.

- Make sure that all communication is clear and necessary.

05
Facilitation activities

5 Facilitation activities

Before you start to plan and organise your facilitation activities, consider the following:

- Who is your audience?
- What is their existing knowledge?
- Is the location and timing of the activity correct?

Valuing individual differences

Some people take to the idea of change more readily than others and different people work and learn in different ways. Some individuals like to develop ideas through activities and discussion while others prefer to have time to think by themselves. We are all different and need to be valued for those differences to ensure the best possible outcome.

As a facilitator, you should recognise and value the individual differences of the participants in your group and build information and activities into your workshop that accommodate all learning styles.

The facilitation tools and techniques that follow are only a handful of the activities you can use, so don't be afraid to try out new ideas other than those listed here!

Communication questionnaire

People have different preferences for how they communicate and how they wish to be communicated with. When working with groups, it is important to consider the different needs and styles. You should also be aware of your own style and biases and try to understand and relate to those who may have styles that are different to yours.

Aim

To help you or members of a group to:

- identify preferences in communication
- understand how this might be seen by others
- recognise and value differences
- start a dialogue and improve understanding.

How to use

Work your way through the four stages of the questionnaire:

- complete the communication questionnaire on the following pages
- score your responses on the response sheet
- consider the descriptions
- consider the implications.

Learning points

- remember to see the person not a 'name badge'
- there are no 'right or wrong' answers, no 'better or worse styles': just differences
- consider asking the group to complete and return the questionnaire to you prior to the workshop. This will give you time to prepare for the discussions.

Complete the questionnaire

- find a quiet space where you will not be disturbed
- work your way through the communication questionnaire
- consider each statement and answer yes or no
- answer as yourself - not as you think you ought to be or would wish to be, not as a manager, clinician, secretary, partner, mother, father, son, daughter, etc - just be yourself!
- try to give an answer to all the questions
- there is no time limit but do not dwell too long on each question.

Complete the communication questionnaire

Start here	Yes / No
01 Do you think it is a sign of strength not to show emotions during a crisis?	
02 Do you often interrupt people when you think they are incorrect?	
03 Does it annoy you when people try to cheer you up?	
04 If you ask someone to do something and they do it wrong, do you have a go at them?	
05 When others have little to say are you able to keep a conversation going?	
06 Are you proud of your ability to deal with people?	
07 Do tactful people annoy you because you wish people would say exactly what they mean?	
08 When you are down in the dumps, do lively people make you feel even worse?	
09 Do you try to sound confident even when you are unsure about the facts?	
10 Are you impatient with people who like to discuss their motives?	
11 Do you think that your feelings are too deep to discuss with others?	

	Yes / No
12 Do you keep quiet when you feel you may offend someone?	
13 Are you diplomatic when you have to tell others to do something against their will?	
14 Does it bother you when others correct your mistakes?	
15 Do you find it difficult to discuss your problems with others?	
16 Are you embarrassed by people who talk about their feelings?	
17 Do you believe people when they ask you if you are all right?	
18 Do you find it hard to admit to your mistakes?	
19 Do you believe that people take advantage of those who are considerate?	
20 Do you value good manners in others?	
21 Do you feel immediately inclined to tell others when something exciting happens to you?	
22 Do you hate to be taken for a ride?	
23 Do you pride yourself on your ability to put up with setbacks?	
24 If someone asked you not to disturb them would you feel hurt?	

	Yes / No
25 Are you often first to speak when an opinion is requested?	
26 Do you enjoy being provocative?	
27 Do you think that being blunt is harmful?	
28 Do you get bored with conversations that don't concern you?	
29 Do you feel that people don't understand you?	
30 Do you like to be the centre of attention?	
31 Do you treat conversations as a chance to test your mettle against others?	
32 If a colleague has a different opinion from yours, will you try to win them over to your point of view?	
33 Do you think that people should keep their problems to themselves?	
34 Do you find it hard to keep a secret?	
35 Do you ignore people when they make you angry?	
36 If a colleague is unhappy would you actively discuss their problems?	
37 If you have a problem would you silently worry about it, even during an evening out?	
38 Does it annoy you to hear someone else dominating a conversation?	

	Yes / No
39 Do you worry about whether other people like you?	
40 Do you resent being asked what you are thinking or feeling?	
41 Do you think that your colleagues ought to know what makes you tick?	
42 Do you visibly show your emotions?	
43 Would you hate to show your distress in front of a colleague?	
44 When you have some time alone, do you spend much of it on the telephone?	
45 Do you find advice from others irritating?	
46 Will you say almost anything to fill a lull in a conversation?	
47 Do you see it as your responsibility to keep other people happy?	
48 Do you often find other people oversensitive?	

Lilley R., Davies G., Cain B., 1999, The PCG Team Builder
A workbook for the health service and primary care team

Score your responses on the response sheet

• Transfer your 'yes' and 'no' answers for each of the 48 statements to the relevant boxes.

• Add up the number of 'yes' answers for each column and write the total in the blank box at the bottom of each column.

• Each score will represent how you conform to the particular style of communication. If you score six or more 'yes' answers for a category then this suggests that you have a natural tendency to use this style.

Response sheet					
04	02	03	05	01	06
07	09	08	21	10	12
17	14	11	24	16	13
19	18	15	28	23	20
22	25	29	30	33	27
26	32	35	34	36	39
31	38	37	44	40	41
48	45	42	46	43	47
Total number of times you answered yes					
Aggressive	Dominating	Worrying	Talkative	Quietly confident	Hinting

Consider the descriptions

Style	Positives	Negatives
Aggressive	Doesn't get pushed around Clear Focused Results orientated	Uses conversations as a duel to be won Can be argumentative (and likes it) Tries to gain dominance
Dominating	Has a view on everything Usually 'expert' in one area Can step in and take charge Always joins in	Can 'put down' less able people Takes over conversations Not always inclusive of quieter members
Worrying	Always makes allowances Highly emotional Risk analyser	Can be negative Appears withdrawn when thinking Needs time to make decision Emotionally draining

Style	Positives	Negatives
Talkative	Easy to get on with Lots of friends Sociable Non-threatening Sense of humour	Talks too much about nothing Lots of friends Uncomfortable with short silences Talks over quieter members of the group
Quietly confident	Seen as emotionally stable Tower of strength Used as sounding board Confidential	Can be seen as aloof Takes too much on Risk of burnout Can be too self critical
Hinting	Influences from behind Quiet and thoughtful Gets on with most people	Avoids conflict Doesn't say what they truly mean Can be seen as manipulative by more direct communicators

Consider the implications

Consider the implications for **your own development** and facilitation style.

Consider how:

- others may see you
- your style may cause tension for others
- you can use your strengths
- to avoid the traps your style may cause.

Look at the other descriptions and consider how you can:

- make others more comfortable
- observe and learn how others respond to you
- make changes to improve communications with individuals who you have the most 'difficulty' with.

Consider the implications for group development. Ask each member of the group to consider, as individuals, the questions and then, as a group think about:

- What are the problems and strengths of 'style alike' or 'style different' groups?
- What is our group strength?
- Where are the gaps?
- What does this indicate?
- What should we do?

Assessing cause and effect

Aim
Ishikawa diagrams (shown on the next page) are used to:

- display cause and effect by stating a problem and listing possible causes and demonstrating the relationships of the possible causes

- ensure that all factors have been considered when analysing a particular problem in depth or thinking through a new idea.

Preparation
You will need to think carefully about the 'effect' i.e. the situation, problem under consideration, or new idea.

- Discuss, define and agree a draft with the design team before the meeting

- Discuss, define and agree with participants at the workshop

How to use
- Ensure all participants are clear about the 'effect'
- Draw a broad arrow from left to right towards the 'effect' box
- Decide on the headings for the branch arrows
- Work with each arrow in turn and get the group to list all possible causes or factors on Post-it notes. Ask participants to place them on the appropriate arrow
- Work with each of the branch arrows in turn and group related thoughts
- Look for gaps and re-address if necessary

Example of Ishikawa diagrams

method   equipment

Effect

environment   people   material

Case study: CT Scanning Midlands

method
- some patients on waiting lists no longer need scans
- wasted slots
- scans booked at last minute - patients cannot attend
- patients booked for 'specialist slots' - multiple waiting lists to manage
- reporting happens in batches - delays in reporting

equipment
- CT scanner only used 9-5 on week days for non-urgent cases

Delays in diagnosis when CT scan required

environment
- only one reporting / viewing room in scanner suite - delays reporting
- no preparation or recovery area - takes up scanner time

people
- patients DNA - wasted slots
- few radiographers trained for contrast injections - delays waiting for radiologist
- secretarial support only weekdays and Sat am - delays in reporting

materials
- no problems identified

Tips

Ensure everyone knows what each of the terms mean

- Equipment can be described as fixed or mobile e.g. rooms, photocopiers, fax machines

- Materials are consumables e.g. stationery, syringes

- People are users, patients, carers, staff, public etc.

Trios

This is relatively easy. It is good for starting up an event and getting people mixing and is a powerful technique for identifying problem areas. The size of the group does not matter.

Aim

- To generate ideas about three questions related to the service

- To enable staff to talk to and share ideas with others who may not be known to them

Preparation

- Three carefully thought out questions such as:
  (A) What problems do patients experience with our service?
  (B) What problems do carers experience with our service?
  (C) What problems do our staff experience with our service?

- Time allowed: 30 minutes

- A pen and Post-it notes for each participant

- Three flip chart stands with one of the questions written on each

How to use

- Ask each participant to find two others they do not know well and form a trio
- Each person in the trio introduces themselves then spends five minutes quietly by themselves addressing each of the three questions
- Each thought or suggestion is written on a Post-it note
  - one thought per Post-it note
  - labelled clearly A, B or C according to which question it addresses
  - participants can generate as many separate Post-it notes as they wish
- After five minutes, allocate one person in the trio A, another B and the third C
- The A person collects and discusses all the A comments from the other two in the trio, ensuring they fully understand their point of view and meaning. Person B collects all the B comments and person C collects all the C comments
- All the A people gather at the A flip chart, all the B people gather at the B flip chart and all the C people gather at the C flip chart
- At each flip chart, the comments are grouped into common themes
- One person feeds back from each of the three flip charts

Station rounds

This activity helps everyone to play an active role.

Aim

- To generate ideas related to the problem or issue
- To give everyone a chance to comment

Preparation

Before the meeting:

- identify and agree four issues to focus on
- state the issues as questions, for example:
  - how can we prevent delays for our patients getting an appointment?
  - how can we prevent delays for our patients once they get into our department?
  - how can we ensure that we best utilise the knowledge and skills of our staff?
  - how can we improve communication between others in the system?

At the meeting:

- allow at least two hours
- one flip chart and stand in each of the four corners of the room
- each of the flip charts has one of the four issue questions written on it
- a different coloured flip chart pen on each of the four flip charts
- lots of wall space around the flip charts to attach completed sheets
- allocate the participants into four groups. Often professional groups working together will prompt more discussion e.g. doctors, nurses, managers, technical staff.

How to use
You will need four rounds and a feedback session.

Round one: 15 minutes

- One group of staff is allocated to each of the flip charts and the colour of the pen in that corner
- Each group selects a 'station master' who will stay at the station for each of the rounds
- For 15 minutes the group address the issue at their station
- The station master records their comments and suggestions on the flip chart using the coloured pen allocated to that group
- At the end of 15 minutes the groups rotate clockwise to the next flip chart and the next issue question, **taking their coloured pen with them**

Round two: 20 minutes
- The groups give their pen to the next station master
- The second station master summarises the comments and suggestions of the previous group
- Any additions from the new group are added in the new coloured pen
- At the end of 20 minutes the groups of staff rotate clockwise to the next flip chart and the next issue question, **again taking their pen with them**

Round three: 20 minutes
- The groups give their pen to the third station master
- The third station master summarises the comments and suggestions of the previous group
- Any additions from the new group are added in the new coloured pen
- At the end of 20 minutes the groups of staff rotate clockwise to the next flip chart and the next issue question, **again taking their pen with them**

Round four: 20 minutes
- The groups give their pen to the fourth station master
- The fourth station master summarises the comments and suggestions of the previous group
- Any additions from the new group are added in the new coloured pen

Feedback
- At the end of the four rounds, the station masters feed back the collective comments of all four groups

Tips
- Use four support facilitators as station masters if available. This allows all participants to address and contribute to all issues
- Ask the station masters to record comments and suggestions as actions

Encouraging creativity
Creativity has to be helped. It involves connecting streams of thinking that are not usually connected.

Aim
- To help the group think differently about the issue or problem
- Some people will find this easier, more comfortable and more enjoyable than others - value the differences

Learning points
- The most creative idea may come by looking at the topic from an outrageous point
- Laughter will be the natural physiological reaction to this new connection in mind - encourage your group to enjoy it

Be someone else

Get the group to think about the topic from the point of view of someone else not normally related to the topic. Examples of 'someone else' include:

- different teams e.g. racing car pit crew, airline cabin crew
- different people e.g. a six-year old child, parent of small children, a homeless person
- different roles e.g. junior school teacher, antique collector, sailor, politician, editor of a professional journal, librarian
- different animals e.g. horse, cat, wolf
- manager of a different service e.g. fast-food restaurant, dry cleaning shop, hotel, rent-a-car company, zoo.

Mental benchmarking

Select a business or industry at random. Describe that business or industry in terms of:

- what the different areas of their work are
- what they do well
- what is natural for them
- how this can be applied to your service issue or problem.

De Bono's Six Thinking Hats®

Use De Bono's Six Thinking Hats® to encourage creative ideas and evaluate those ideas. De Bono's hats give value to all our different thoughts.

Evaluating ideas

The more ideas and options that are generated, the more likely they are to develop creative solutions to difficult problems. However, effective methods are required to make the transition between tens or hundreds of ideas and a few powerful actions. Evaluating ideas gives you five ways to help a group evaluate the options they have generated.

Note: there may be some obvious actions that everyone agrees with and improvements could be made straight away. Just do it!

Aim
To evaluate a list of options or ideas regarding a problem or situation.

Method
• To determine the time for implementation and priority of the favoured ideas

Preparation
For all the following methods:
• prepare flip charts of all the ideas generated, each with no more than five ideas, in large clear handwriting
• ensure all ideas or options to be considered are clearly understood by participants
• remind the group of the objectives of the workshop and of the problems that have been identified.

Sticky dots

- Use when there are lots of ideas or options (>50) to be considered
- Give each participant 10 sticky dots in each of four colours: green, yellow, red and black
- Explain the significance of the different coloured dots:
  - *green:* great idea and it can be implemented within a week
  - *yellow:* great idea but it will take up to a month to implement
  - *red:* great idea but needs planning and will take up to three months to implement
  - *black:* great idea but needs a lot of planning and will take over three months to implement
- Ask the participants to stick their dots according to how they rate the ideas presented
- They can stick all on one idea if they feel very strongly about it or distribute the entire colour amongst ten different ideas with one dot each
- Examine the results and look for the ideas with most dots
- Agree next steps

Voting
Use when there are a limited number of ideas or options (<10) to consider.

- Each participant can vote for only three of the ideas
- Each participant votes by writing at the side of each idea on the flip chart allocating a score:
  - 3 to the most preferred ideas
  - 2 to the second choice
  - 1 to the third choice
- No points to the other ideas
- Add up the scores to find the chosen idea
- Agree next steps

Traffic light assessment
Use when you need an opinion about every idea.

- Each participant has three coloured pens: red, yellow and green
- Explain the meaning of the three colours:
  - *green* means full support
  - *yellow* means OK
  - *red* means not happy
- Ask each participant to mark each idea in the relevant colour with their initials to get a clear idea of everyone's thoughts
- Agree next steps

TPN analysis

Use to determine what the group can do themselves and whether the ideas are within the control of the group.

- For each idea the group decides if it is:
  T - totally within the control of the group
  P - partially within the control of the group
  N - not within the control of the group
- The decision can be reached by discussion if the group is small or participants writing TPN against the ideas or options on the flip charts
- Agree next steps:
  - decide how the Ts can be taken forward
  - identify who else needs to be involved to move the Ps forward
  - decide where the Ns need to be referred

Must, should and could do

Use when a number of ideas or options needs to be prioritised.

- For each idea, the group decides what:
  - must be done
  - should be done
  - could be done
- The decision can be reached by:
  - discussion if the group is small
  - participants writing 'must', 'should' or 'could' against the ideas on the flip charts
- Transfer the 'must be done' and 'should be done' on to Post-it notes
- Arrange the Post-it notes in chronological order with the 'must be done' ideas first to develop a draft plan for next steps
- Agree next steps

Next steps

After the issues have been identified, ideas for possible solutions generated and potential solutions evaluated, you need to help the group plan for testing and implementing the chosen ideas. Consider:

- Defined actions
- Allocated responsibilities
- Timescales
- Large tasks broken down into smaller, more manageable ones
- Agreed priority to tackling tasks
- Dates of when and how the progress towards the actions will be reviewed

Aim

To have a clear plan of:

- what action needs to be taken including the priority
- who will undertake the action
- when the action is to be taken
- how the action will be taken.

Resource / impact matrix
Preparation
- Flip chart paper and Post-it notes for all participants
- List of all actions agreed from previous generating or prioritising exercise
- Clarification and agreement of the terms and the implied timescales
- Quick wins (short term, low resource implications but high impact)
- Soft targets (short term, low resource implications but lower impact)
- Challenging tasks (longer term, higher resource implications but high impact)
- Hold-offs (longer term, high resource implications and low impacts)

Method
The group plots each of their proposed actions on this matrix. Look for the:
- quick wins to create energy and momentum for change
- soft targets to be tackled after quick wins
- challenging tasks - generally those ideas that create the greatest improvement
- hold-offs that are different to the challenging tasks - best left until other changes have been made or circumstances change.

Resource/Impact Matrix

Not urgent
Low impact

Soft targets

Hold-offs

Challenging tasks

Urgent
High impact

Quick wins

| | Low resources
Short term | Med. resources
Med. term
(6 months +) | High resources
Long term
(12 months +) |

Judge ideas against agreed criteria such as:
Cost, practicality, realism, fit with desired objectives etc.

Planning the next steps

Use this simple framework when there is a small number of actions generated for each group of actions from the resource/impact matrix.

Method

- Identify each action generated and record one per Post-it note
- Work with the group and arrange the Post-it notes in chronological order
- Consider which actions can be taken quickly and which should be tackled over a longer timescale
- Check for gaps and missing actions
- Identify who will be responsible for each action and exactly what is required of them
- Write names of those who will be responsible against each action
- Put timescales above the Post-it notes
- Transfer onto action sheet
- Make sure all involved have their own copy of the agreed next steps
- Agree the process for reviewing progress

Example of a simple plan for the next steps											
What	**Who**	**Notes**	**Sep**	**Oct**	**Nov**	**Dec**	**Jan**	**Feb**	**Mar**	**Apr**	**May**
Detailed description of each action	JP KC DR										
Action	HB										
Action	JH LG										
Action	JP										
Action	KK										
Action	SB										
Action	KK SB										
Action	KS										

Model for Improvement

Many of the actions involve testing improvement ideas in Plan, Do, Study and Act cycles (PDSA) before implementing. The Model for Improvement has been a fundamental framework underpinning many improvement programmes and projects.

Aim

To help improvement groups to:

- set clear aims and targets
- develop a few specific measures to show if a change is an improvement
- identify the changes that are most likely to make an improvement in high risk services
- test change ideas before implementing them.

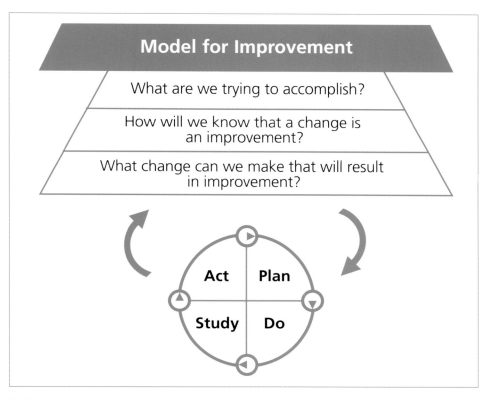

Reference: Langley G, Nolan K, Nolan T, Norman C, Provost L, (1996),
The Improvement Guide: a practical approach to enhancing organisational
performance, Jossey Bass Publishers, San Francisco

06

Your questions answered

6 Your questions answered

If you are new to facilitation, you probably have lots of questions about the role of the facilitator in group meetings and how to get the most out of a facilitated workshop. In this section we address some of the key questions you may have.

Question: I have been to some workshops where the facilitator has used an 'ice breaker'. I enjoy them but I know not everyone does. Should I include one in my workshop?

Answer: You're right in your observation that ice breakers are not everybody's cup of tea. When deciding whether to use an ice breaker in your workshop, think carefully about:

- Who will be there? Some professional groups dislike ice breakers more than others.

- How long have you got? If the session is not long, you really want to get on with the work.

- Will this group meet regularly and do you want this group to develop relationships, have fun and break down barriers?

If you are using an ice breaker in your workshop, consider the objective of doing so and make sure you communicate this with the group. Ice breakers are usually used to get the group mixing, talking and finding things out about each other.

If you decide that an icebreaker is right, there are plenty to choose from but here is a simple one called 'human bingo' that you can use with a large group.

Have fun, use your imagination and change the categories according to the group, time of day etc.

Example ice breaker - human bingo

Instructions for human bingo:

- Find 24 different people to match the characteristics on the card (see example)

- No one can be used more than once and you cannot use yourself

- Write one name against each of the characteristics

- The 'winner' will be the person who fills all the squares or the most in the given time (just like in bingo!)

Human Bingo

Someone with a birthday in March	Someone with a 'comic' tie or 'comic' socks	Someone wearing contact lenses	Someone who has had a barium meal x-ray
Someone with green eyes	Someone who has given up smoking	Someone who has sat on a jury	Someone younger than you
Someone who has eaten sushi	Someone who has ridden a camel	Someone who has not brought a laptop with them	Someone who has been jogging in the last week
Someone who has swum naked	Someone who has been parascending	Someone you did not know before today	Someone shorter than you
Someone not born in England	Someone who will give you a hug	Someone who has been to China	Someone with longer hair than you
Someone taller than you	Someone who plays an instrument	Someone who has been white water rafting	Someone who has sung karaoke

Alternative ice breakers

You may want to use an activity that starts the work, breaks the ice and generates energy all at the same time. Here is an idea you could try:

• Get participants into pairs or small groups, ask them to introduce themselves and then to take a few minutes to answer some relevant questions putting answers on flip charts. Use questions about:

  – The past - what has surprised you about... e.g. the outcome from the process mapping sessions?

  – The present - what would be the first thing a Martian would notice about... e.g. our department / surgery / hospital?

  – The future - what would you do if you had total power?

Question: I have heard a lot of facilitation terms used that I don't understand. Can you explain them to me in one easy sentence and where can I find out more?

Answer: We will try but it may take more than one sentence! We have put some of the key terms together with a brief description of what they mean in the table on the opposite page. You might also like to try using the internet to search for more information on facilitation terms that you've heard about. Type the name of the term you are interested in into the search engine and see what comes up!

Term	Simple description
Graphic facilitation	This is the use of graphics or drawings in meetings. This helps participants with a 'visual language' that can often be more powerful than the spoken or written word. Graphics are also very useful for groups of people with different levels of language, numeracy or literacy skills.
Polarity management	Polarities are sets of opposites that cannot function independently. Because the two sides of a polarity are interdependent, you cannot choose one as a solution and neglect the other - you need to manage them. The objective of polarity management is to get the best of both opposites whilst avoiding the limits of each.
World café	World café is a way to quickly explore topics and come to a shared understanding within a medium sized or large group. It involves rotating through a series of small discussion groups. Just like going from table to table in a café!
Open space	This is a way of working that allows individuals to lead whatever discussion topics they are interested in. These suggested sessions are first shared at the event and then everyone has the choice to go to whatever conversation that interests them or to move between groups. This method works well for groups between about 20 and many hundreds.
Appreciative Inquiry	Appreciative Inquiry (AI) is a process that involves people in conversations to recognise and build on what they like and appreciate. It encourages people to reflect and learn from what has worked well for them, times when they felt good and achieved a really good performance and then apply the learning to current problems.

Question: How do I improve my facilitation skills?

Answer: Use the facilitation ideas in the activities section of this handy guide. Use the PDSA cycles to test the different facilitation tools and techniques for yourself. Also, you should ask yourself the following three questions:

- What am I trying to achieve?
- How will I know a change is an improvement?
  - Consider yourself - how you feel, what you see and hear.
  - Consider the group - interaction, body language, evaluation forms.
  - Consider your colleagues - debrief, comments.
- What changes can I make that will result in the improvement that I seek?
  - Use PDSA cycles to test the different facilitation tools and techniques for yourself. Start by working with a 'friendly' group and learn in order to build your confidence.

Question: How can I ensure good conversations and reflections?

Answer: Preparation is everything! You will be bringing together a variety of different people: those with commitment, those with different views, those with the authority to act and those with special skills. Your job is to create a climate in which no one feels excluded or discounted, allowing participants to share deeply-held beliefs, feeling safe to share and tackle disagreements gracefully.

Nothing should be done for the individual at the expense of the whole group or for the whole group at the expense of the individual. Remember to:

- Seat people at round tables if at all possible where they can all listen to each other and no one is at the 'head'

- Encourage people to practice non-judgemental listening and be curious about why people see things differently from them, rather than judging their views

- Give people a voice by allowing enough time for contributions whether they are brainstorming, sharing stories or in dialogue

- Build in time for reflection

Question: What are the alternatives to 'same time and same place' meetings?

Answer: There is often a need for quite large groups to work together over a set period of time. This causes challenges as we are conditioned to work in a face-to-face manner and the answer to many improvement initiatives is to 'have a meeting'. This means people leaving their place of work and travelling to be together. This causes a struggle to allocate the time from busy days.

It becomes much harder to bring everyone together when the size of the group grows and we work with people from different departments, organisations or even different parts of the country.

Technology can help. It works best when members of the group have met face-to-face at least once and are at the performing stage of group development. This means the group is well organised, understands its purpose and is developing well. If the group is not well developed it may make things worse, so beware!

The technology is available, but some staff do not have access to all of it, so agree with the group what is possible. Talk to the people in your organisation who look after the telephone services or the IT. They will know what is available, what is being planned and be able to recommend how you can arrange to use it.

Model for the use of time and place	
Quadrant 1: Same place, same time • meetings • workshops	**Quadrant 2:** Same place, any time • notice boards, etc.
Quadrant 3: Any place, same time • telephone, conference calls • video conference • chat room technology • 'sharing' software	**Quadrant 4:** Any place, any time • email • ebulletin and discussion boards • digital workspaces

Fundamentals for Quality Improvement

The NHS Institute for Innovation and Improvement has developed a suite of publications that will assist you in finding innovative ways to improve the quality, productivity and efficiency of patient care you provide.

Quality and Service Improvement Tools Online

A web-based library of 80+ quality and service improvement tools that will enable you to expand your knowledge of tried-and-tested tools and techniques for improving quality and productivity. You can access the tools at www.institute.nhs.uk/qualitytools

A Step by Step Guide to Tackling Your Challenges

This guide maps some of the key challenges you have told us the health service is facing against a range of quality and improvement tools and products developed by the NHS Institute to support the NHS in